아서 스타터 워크북 04

아서

가을에 빠져들다

글·그림 마크 브라운

롱테일북스

등장인물

D.W.

메리 무 카우를 좋아하는 아서의 여동생. 아서를 괴롭히는 게 취미이다.

팔

아서 가족의 반려견. 사고뭉치이지만 아서를 잘 따른다.

버스터

아서의 가장 친한 친구. 탐정 놀이와 외계인을 좋아하는 특이한 성격의 소유자.

브레인

아서의 친구들 중 가장 똑똑한 친구. 특히 수학과 과학을 제일 잘한다.

프랜신

무슨 운동이든 잘하는 아서의 친구. 활달한 성격으로 리더십이 있다.

Contents

Eliza's
APE JAM
TOLON

아서와 D.W.는 아침 식사를 마치고 있었습니다.

"나는 오늘 네게 맡길 일이 있단다, 아서." 아빠가 말했습니다.

"나는 네가 뒤뜰에 있는 낙엽을 긁어모아 줬으면 해."

"오늘은 D.W.가 낙엽을 모으는 법을 배우기에 좋은 날이 아닐까요?"
아서가 물었습니다.
아빠가 그의 고개를 저었습니다. "D.W.는 다른 일로 나를 도와줄 거야."

아서는 앙상한 나무를 올려다보았습니다.

“이건 모두 네 잘못이야.” 그가 말했습니다.

그러고 나서 그는 갈퀴질을 하기 시작했습니다.

낙엽은 땅에 달라붙어 있는 것 같았습니다.
아서는 더 세게 갈퀴질을 했습니다.

곧 그는 작은 낙엽 더미를 만들었습니다.

"어떻게 생각해, 팔?" 그가 물었습니다.

팔은 킁킁거리며 냄새를 맡았습니다. 그러더니 녀석은 자신의 입으로 낙엽 한 잎을 주워서 그것을 그 더미에 더했습니다.

아서는 계속 갈퀴질을 했습니다.

더미는 조금 더 커졌습니다.

“이건 정말 힘든 일이야.” 그가 팔에게 말했습니다.

“아무래도 우리는 좀 쉬어야 할 것 같아.”

아서와 팔은 낙엽 더미로 뛰어들었습니다.

그다음에 그들은 뛰고 또 뛰었습니다.

곧 낙엽은 다시 마당에 온통 흩어졌습니다.

“아서, 너 뭐 하고 있니?” 프랜신이 물었습니다.

그녀는 버스터와 브레인과 함께 걸어왔습니다.

“나는 갈퀴질을 하는 중이야.” 아서가 말했습니다.

“너는 그리 잘하고 있지 않은걸.” 브레인이 말했습니다.

“이건 힘을 적절하게 쓰는지에 관한 문제야. 자, 내가 보여 줄게.”

브레인이 갈퀴질을 하기 시작했습니다.

“내가 어떻게 팔꿈치를 굽히는지 보이지?” 그가 말했습니다.

“응.” 아서가 말했습니다. “더 보여 줘.”

이제 프랜신의 차례였습니다. “이건 그렇게 힘들지 않아.” 그녀가 말했습니다.

“단지 체계성과 근육의 힘만 있으면 돼.”

"와!" 버스터가 말했습니다. "이건 우리나라에서 가장 큰 낙엽 더미가 되겠어—아니 어쩌면 전 세계에서 말이야."

마침내, 모든 낙엽을 모았습니다.

“봤니?” 브레인이 말했습니다. “일은 바로 이렇게 하는 거야.”

아서가 고개를 끄덕였습니다. “고마워, 얘들아. 완벽해.”

“정말 완벽해!”

Activities

영어 원서를 총 세 개의 파트로 나누어,
각 파트별로 다양한 액티비티를 담았습니다.

각 파트의 영어 원서 페이지는 롱테일북스에서 출간된
'롱테일 에디션'을 기준으로 합니다!

Vocabulary Part 1

마치다, 끝내다

finish

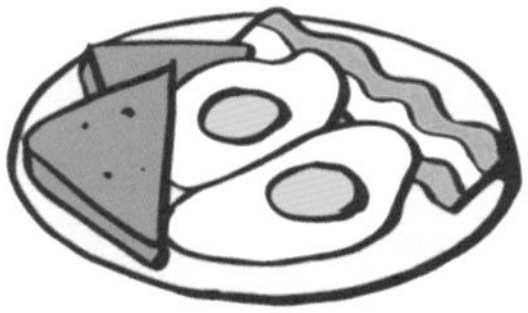

아침 식사

breakfast

일, 직업

job

갈퀴질을 하다, 갈퀴로 모으다

rake

나뭇잎 (복수형 leaves)

leaf

뒤뜰, 뒷마당

backyard

시간, 때

time

배우다

learn

머리

head

다른, 그 밖의

other

일, 것

thing

비어 있는, 빈

empty

잘못, 책임

fault

(~인 것) 같다, (~처럼) 보이다

seem

달라붙다

stick

땅

ground

세게, 열심히; 힘든

hard

더미, 무더기

pile

Word Review Part 1

A 알파벳을 바르게 배열하여 그림에 맞게 단어를 완성해 보세요.

1

o j b

j

2

a n l r e

3

c k s i t

B 알파벳을 바르게 써넣어 그림에 알맞은 단어를 완성해 보세요.

1
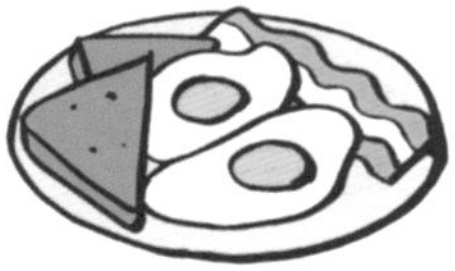

brea k fast

2

f   ni

3

ou   d

C 그림을 보고 알맞은 단어를 퍼즐에서 찾은 뒤, 빈칸에 단어를 써 보세요.

e	m	p	t	y	m	p	v
i	k	i	x	s	w	i	a
d	n	l	w	l	e	a	f
t	p	e	z	j	y	k	t
y	q	i	h	d	r	j	b
n	z	m	e	t	n	y	w
e	x	r	a	k	e	k	z
v	t	q	d	c	m	l	a

1

pile

2

3

4

5

Wrap Up! Part 1

A 이야기의 순서에 맞게 번호를 적어 보세요.

D.W. would help Dad with another job.

Arthur thought that the job was all because of the empty tree.

Arthur had made a little pile of leaves.

1

Dad asked Arthur to rake leaves.

B 각 단어에 알맞은 그림을 찾고, 이를 설명하는 문장을 찾아 바르게 이어 보세요.

breakfast

The empty tree had just a few leaves.

rake

There were leaves all over the backyard.

backyard

Arthur and D.W. were finishing their breakfast.

empty

Arthur started to rake leaves.

C 다음 그림을 보고 아래의 단어를 알맞게 넣어 문장을 완성해 보세요.

hard pile seemed

1 The leaves ________ to be sticking to the ground.

2 It was ________ for Arthur to rake leaves.

3 Arthur raked leaves into a little ________ .

D 책의 내용과 일치하면 TRUE에, 그렇지 않으면 FALSE에 동그라미를 그려 보세요.

1. Arthur and D.W. were having their breakfast. TRUE FALSE
2. D.W. had learned how to rake. TRUE FALSE
3. Arthur said that it was the tree's fault. TRUE FALSE
4. Arthur was digging the ground. TRUE FALSE

E 다음 질문에 대한 알맞은 답을 골라 보세요.

What did Dad want Arthur to do?

a. Shake the tree to make it empty

b. Rake leaves in the backyard

c. Finish his breakfast

Let's Write! Part 1

A 우리말에 맞게 알맞은 짝을 찾아 바르게 연결하고 완성된 문장을 두 번씩 써 보세요.

1 I want you	a little pile of leaves.
2 D.W. will be helping me	with other things.
3 Arthur looked up	at the empty tree.
4 He had made	to rake leaves in the backyard.

1 나는 네가 뒤뜰에 있는 낙엽을 긁어모아 줬으면 해.

I want you to rake leaves in the backyard.

2 D.W.는 다른 일로 나를 도와줄 거야.

3 아서는 앙상한 나무를 올려다보았습니다.

4 그는 작은 낙엽 더미를 만들었습니다.

Vocabulary Part 2

생각하다

think

냄새 맡기; 냄새를 맡다

sniff

줍다, 집어 들다

pick up

입

mouth

더하다, 덧붙이다

add

(수, 양이) 많은

a lot of

휴식 (take a break 쉬다)

break

뛰다, 점프하다

jump

다시, 한 번 더

again

흩뿌리다

scatter

마당, 뜰

yard

걷다; 산책, 걷기

walk

~와 함께

with

문제

question

쓰다, 적용하다

apply

힘

force

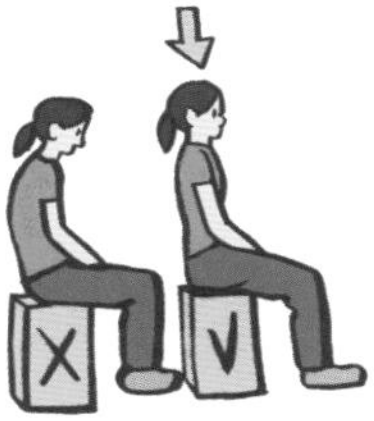

적절히, 제대로

properly

보여 주다; 공연, 대회

show

Word Review Part 2

A 알파벳을 이어서 알맞은 그림과 연결하고, 빈칸에 완성된 단어를 써 보세요.

g

a　　　　　i　　　w

a

y　　　　r　　o　　n

a

f　　h　　　　　d

c

r

s　　　　　　　　e

o

again

B 그림을 보고 같은 색깔의 알파벳을 바르게 배열하여 빈칸에 써 보세요.

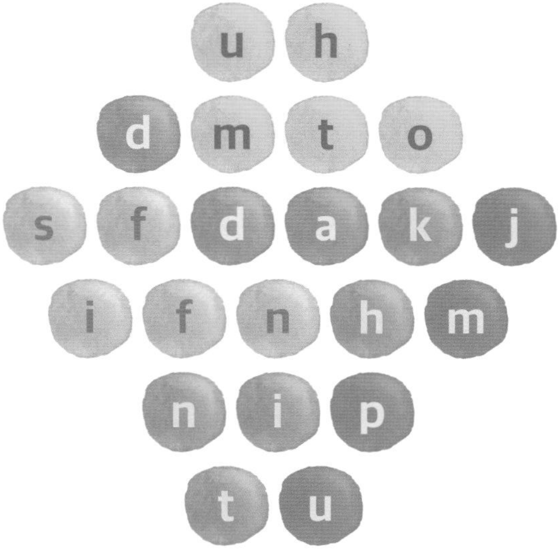

1

mouth

2

3

4

5

A 이야기의 순서에 맞게 번호를 적어 보세요.

Pal helped Arthur make the pile.

Arthur showed the pile to Pal.

Arthur wanted to take a break.

Arthur and Pal kept jumping in the pile.

B 두 개의 문장 중 오른쪽에 있는 그림을 바르게 설명하는 문장을 골라 보세요.

1
ⓐ Pal added a leaf to the pile.
ⓑ Pal took a break.

2
ⓐ Arthur kept raking.
ⓑ Arthur kept picking up leaves.

3
ⓐ Arthur and Pal walked through the leaves.
ⓑ Arthur and Pal jumped in the leaves.

4
ⓐ The leaves were scattered all over the yard.
ⓑ The leaves were piled under the tree.

C 다음 그림을 보고 아래의 단어를 알맞게 넣어 문장을 완성해 보세요.

showed   with   properly

1 Francine came over ________ Buster and the Brain.

2 The Brain told Arthur to apply force ________ .

3 The Brain ________ Arthur how to rake.

D 책의 내용과 일치하면 TRUE에, 그렇지 않으면 FALSE에 동그라미를 그려 보세요.

1 Arthur thought that raking was hard. TRUE FALSE

2 Arthur and Pal didn't take a break. TRUE FALSE

3 Arthur and Pal scattered the leaves all over the yard. TRUE FALSE

4 The Brain thought that Arthur was good at raking. TRUE FALSE

E 다음 질문에 대한 알맞은 답을 골라 보세요.

How did Pal help Arthur?

a He took a break.

b He added a leaf to the pile.

c He kept Arthur's friends away from the backyard.

Let's Write! Part 2

A 오늘 공부한 문장을 따라 써 보세요.

1 녀석은 자신의 입으로 낙엽 한 잎을 주웠습니다.

He picked up a leaf in his mouth.

2 아서는 계속 갈퀴질을 했습니다.

Arthur kept raking.

3 아무래도 우리는 좀 쉬어야 할 것 같아.

Maybe we should take a break.

4. 그들은 뛰고 또 뛰었습니다.

They jumped again and again.

5. 너는 그리 잘하고 있지 않은걸.

You're not doing a very good job.

6. 자, 내가 보여 줄게.

Here, let me show you.

Vocabulary Part 3

시작하다

start

보다

see

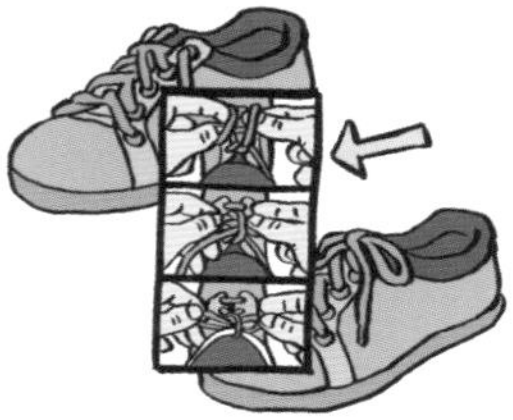

어떻게

how

굽히다, 구부리다

bend

팔꿈치

elbow

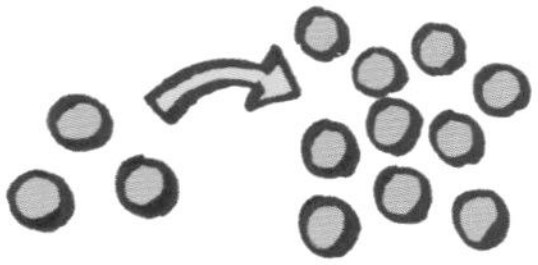

더 많이; 더 많은

more

차례, 순번

turn

체계성, 조직성

organization

근육

muscle

힘

power

나라

country

전체의

whole

세계, 세상

world

모으다

collect

(고개를) 끄덕이다
(과거형 nodded)

nod

고마워하다, 감사하다

thank

모든 사람, 모두

everyone

완벽한

perfect

Word Review Part 3

A 그림을 보고 알파벳 속에서 맞는 단어를 찾아 빈칸에 써 보세요.

moimorebcoaperfectdmjbpthankhcollectqpnmusclebisekgseeln

1
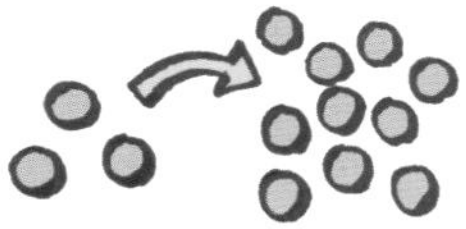

more

2

3

4

5

6

B 그림을 보고 알맞은 단어를 퍼즐에 넣어 완성한 뒤, 빈칸에 단어를 써 보세요.

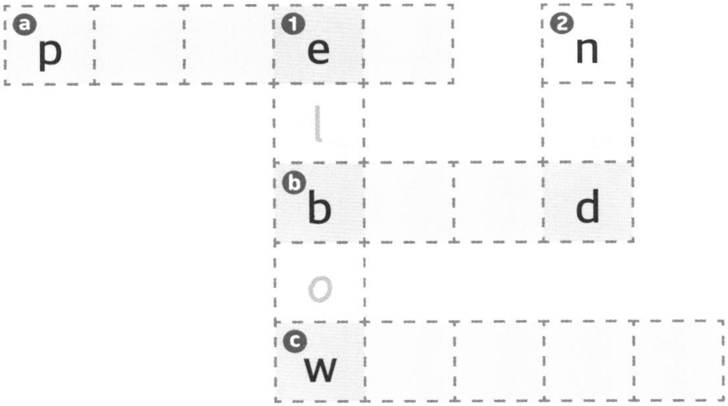

❶

elbow

❷

ⓐ

ⓑ

ⓒ

Wrap Up! Part 3

A 이야기의 순서에 맞게 번호를 적어 보세요.

The Brain showed Arthur how to bend his elbows.

Everyone thought that their pile was perfect.

Buster thought that their pile could be the biggest one.

Francine started raking after the Brain.

B 그림의 각 부분을 올바르게 설명하는 문장을 찾아 빈칸에 맞는 기호를 넣어 보세요.

ⓐ Francine helped Arthur with raking.

ⓑ The Brain took a turn again.

ⓒ All the leaves were collected in the backyard.

ⓓ Arthur loved their pile of leaves.

C 다음 그림을 보고 아래의 단어를 알맞게 넣어 문장을 완성해 보세요.

muscle collected turn

1 Francine took a ______ after the Brain.

2 Francine ______ the leaves.

3 Francine used her ______ power for raking.

D 책의 내용과 일치하면 TRUE에, 그렇지 않으면 FALSE에 동그라미를 그려 보세요.

1. Arthur learned how to bend his elbows from the Brain. TRUE FALSE
2. Buster thought that their pile was not big enough. TRUE FALSE
3. Arthur and his friends collected all the leaves. TRUE FALSE
4. Arthur thanked his friends for helping him rake. TRUE FALSE

E 다음 질문에 대한 알맞은 답을 골라 보세요.

Why did Arthur thank his friends?

a. They took care of Pal.
b. They brought him some snacks.
c. They helped him rake all the leaves.

Let's Write! Part 3

A 우리말에 맞게 네모 안에 있는 단어를 바르게 배열하여 문장을 완성해 보세요.

1 브레인이 갈퀴질을 하기 시작했습니다.

raking 갈퀴질하는 것을	The Brain 브레인이	started 시작했다

The Brain started ______________________.

2 더 보여 줘.

me 내게	more 더	Show 보여 줘

______________________.

3 이제 프랜신의 차례였습니다.

Francine 프랜신이	Now 이제	took a turn ~할 차례였다

______________________.

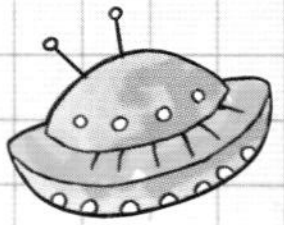

4 이건 그렇게 힘들지 않아.

hard	so	isn't	This
힘든	그렇게	~하지 않다	이것은

____ .

5 이건 가장 큰 낙엽 더미가 되겠어.

could be	the biggest pile	This	of leaves
~이 되겠다	가장 큰 더미가	이것은	낙엽의

____ .

6 마침내, 모든 낙엽을 모았습니다.

all the leaves	Finally,	were collected
모든 낙엽이	마침내	모였다

____ .

Part 1

Word Review

A

1

ojb
job

2

anlre
learn

3

cksit
stick

B

1
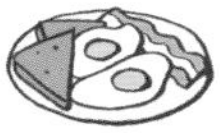
breakfast

2

finish

3

ground

C

e	m	p	t	y	m	p	v
i	k	i	x	s	w	i	a
d	n	l	w	l	e	a	f
t	p	e	z	j	y	k	t
y	q	i	h	d	r	j	b
n	z	m	e	t	n	y	w
e	x	r	a	k	e	k	z
v	t	q	d	c	m	l	a

1

pile

2

head

3

rake

4

leaf

5

empty

Wrap Up!

A

2
D.W. would help Dad with another job.

3
Arthur thought that the job was all because of the empty tree.

4
Arthur had made a little pile of leaves.

1
Dad asked Arthur to rake leaves.

B

- breakfast — Arthur and D.W. were finishing their breakfast.
- rake — Arthur started to rake leaves.
- backyard — There were leaves all over the backyard.
- empty — The empty tree had just a few leaves.

C

1. The leaves seemed to be sticking to the ground.
2. It was hard for Arthur to rake leaves.
3. Arthur raked leaves into a little pile.

D 1 TRUE 2 FALSE 3 TRUE 4 FALSE

E b

Let's Write!

A

1. I want you — to rake leaves in the backyard.
2. D.W. will be helping me — with other things.
3. Arthur looked up — at the empty tree.
4. He had made — a little pile of leaves.

Part 2
Word Review

A

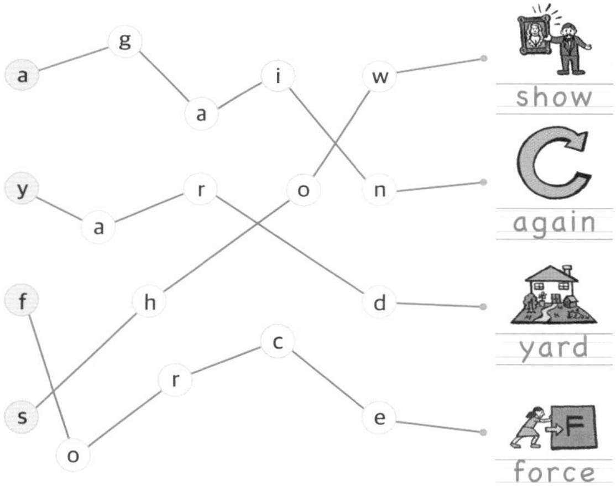

show
again
yard
force

B

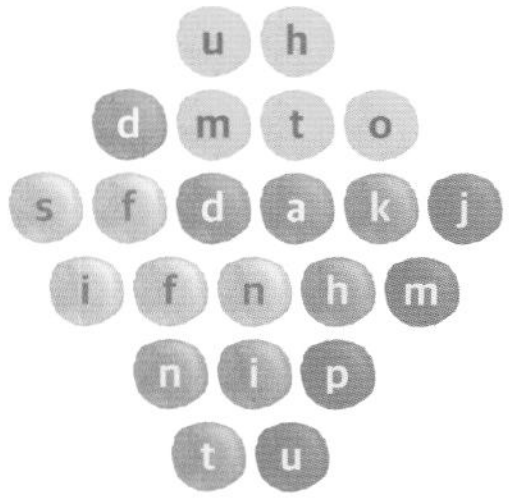

1 
mouth

2 
jump

3 

add

4 
sniff

5 
think

Wrap Up!

A

2 Pal helped Arthur make the pile.

1 Arthur showed the pile to Pal.

3 Arthur wanted to take a break.

4 Arthur and Pal kept jumping in the pile.

B 1 a 2 a 3 b 4 a

C

1 Francine came over with Buster and the Brain.

2 The Brain told Arthur to apply force properly.

3 The Brain showed Arthur how to rake.

D 1 TRUE 2 FALSE 3 TRUE 4 FALSE

E b

Part 3
Word Review

A

moimorebcoaperfectdmjbpthankhcollectqpnmusclebisekgseeln

1

more

2

collect

3

thank

4

perfect

5

muscle

6

see

B

Across: a power, b bend, c world
Down: 1 elbow, 2 nod

1

elbow

2

nod

a

power

b

bend

c

world

Wrap Up!

A

The Brain showed Arthur how to bend his elbows.

Everyone thought that their pile was perfect.

Buster thought that their pile could be the biggest one.

Francine started raking after the Brain.

B

C

1. Francine took a turn after the Brain.
2. Francine collected the leaves.
3. Francine used her muscle power for raking.

D 1 TRUE 2 FALSE 3 TRUE 4 TRUE

E c

Let's Write!

A

1. The Brain started raking.
2. Show me more.
3. Now Francine took a turn.
4. This isn't so hard.
5. This could be the biggest pile of leaves.
6. Finally, all the leaves were collected.

More Arthur Stories to Read!